Drum Kit 4

Pieces & Exercises

for Trinity College London exams
2014-2019

Grades 7 & 8

Published by
Trinity College London

Registered Office:
89 Albert Embankment
London SE1 7TP UK

T +44 (0)20 7820 6100
F +44 (0)20 7820 6161
E music@trinitycollege.co.uk
www.trinitycollege.co.uk

Registered in the UK
Company no. 02683033
Charity no. 1014792

Second impression, April 2014

Music processed by Moira Roach.
Printed in England by Halstan, Amersham, Bucks.

Trinity College London graded drum kit examinations

Introduction

The aim of the Trinity College London drum kit syllabus is the development of versatile musicians, confident to play with authority, creativity and sensitivity across a broad range of styles and able to read and interpret drum charts with conviction and flair.

Drum kit examinations

Candidates are required to perform:

- two exercises. The first is chosen by the candidate, the other is chosen by the examiner from the remaining two exercises.
- two pieces from Group A (played with a backing track, with or without click, or live piano accompaniment)
- one piece from Group B (unaccompanied)
- two supporting tests

Exercises are specially written pieces that involve all the rudiments set for a particular grade (see cumulative rudiments grid). These rudiments are set out at the beginning of each grade section. Candidates will be required to learn these in order to be able to play the exercises.

Group A pieces have full backing accompaniment on CD, with and without click track, or piano accompaniment where appropriate. Candidates will be marked on their ability to interpret a typical drum chart and interact with the backing in terms of time-keeping, phrasing, soloing etc.

Group B pieces are unaccompanied.

Supporting Tests explore the candidate's perception and broader knowledge.

For full details on how to enter for an exam, venue equipment, supporting tests and how the exams are assessed, please refer to the current syllabus booklet which can be found at www.trinitycollege.co.uk

Drum kit rudiments

Rudiment / Grade	Grade 1	Grade 2	Grade 3	Grade 4	Grade 5	Grade 6	Grade 7	Grade 8
Single strokes	✓	✓	✓	✓	✓	✓	✓	✓
Double strokes	✓	✓	✓	✓	✓	✓	✓	✓
Single paradiddle	✓	✓	✓	✓	✓	✓	✓	✓
Flam		✓	✓	✓	✓	✓	✓	✓
Drag		✓	✓	✓	✓	✓	✓	✓
Four stroke ruff		✓	✓	✓	✓	✓	✓	✓
Five stroke roll			✓	✓	✓	✓	✓	✓
Seven stroke roll			✓	✓	✓	✓	✓	✓
Nine stroke roll			✓	✓	✓	✓	✓	✓
Flam tap				✓	✓	✓	✓	✓
Flam accent				✓	✓	✓	✓	✓
Flamacue				✓	✓	✓	✓	✓
Flam paradiddle				✓	✓	✓	✓	✓
Double paradiddle				✓	✓	✓	✓	✓
Paradiddle-diddle				✓	✓	✓	✓	✓
Drag and stroke					✓	✓	✓	✓
Double drag and stroke					✓	✓	✓	✓
Drag paradiddle					✓	✓	✓	✓
Single ratamacue					✓	✓	✓	✓
Double ratamacue					✓	✓	✓	✓
Triple ratamacue					✓	✓	✓	✓
Triple paradiddle						✓	✓	✓
Reverse paradiddle						✓	✓	✓
Pata fla fla							✓	✓
Swiss army triplet							✓	✓
Inward paradiddle							✓	✓

Drum kit notation key

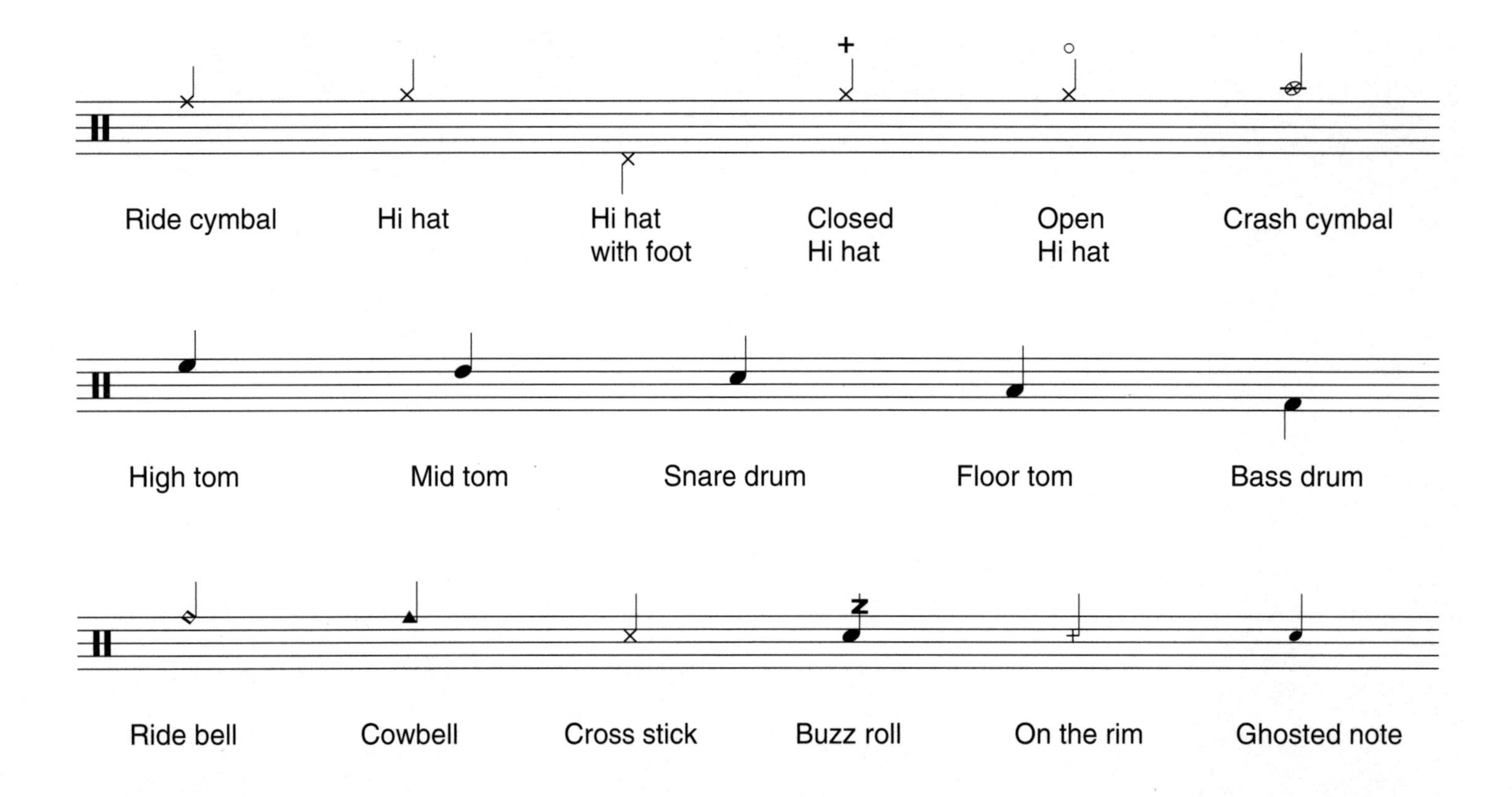

Please note that the notation used for ride cymbal (and bell), crash cymbal and cross stick has changed from that used in previous Trinity College London exam publications. Drum kit notation varies between different publishers/ arrangers but the key above is becoming more consistently used.

Performance notes

General note for both grades

Where a crash cymbal appears at the start of a bar and is followed by one-bar repeat signs (𝄎), the crash cymbal should **not** be played in the repeat bars. If a crash cymbal is required, it will be notated above the repeated bar in question. This is universally accepted as standard drum kit notation and it is the aim of the Trinity College London syllabus to encourage students to become familiar with what they will be confronted with in the real world of drum kit performance.

All repeats, including those within *da capo* and *dal segno* sections, should be observed in drum kit examinations (unless otherwise stated).

Candidates may use the backing track with or without clicks in the examination. Crossing Paths must be played with the click track.

Grade 7

Paul Francis Exercise nos. 1, 2 and 3

These exercises place sticking patterns over an ostinato foot pattern in $\frac{3}{4}$ time. Many patterns phase against the established time and players should aim for the neatest alignment of feet and hands possible, practising the individual sticking patterns along with the feet to build confidence to begin with. Ensure also that the sound between hands is well balanced too.

Be careful to keep time strict, particularly when moving between different subdivisions of the beat, especially triplet quavers/eighth notes and semiquavers/sixteenth notes. Grace notes should be clearly contrasted in terms of volume and all accents should be distinctly brought out. Bounced double strokes should be consistent in terms of time and volume and all written rolls must be played open, not buzzed. Dynamic contrast should be clearly observed and presents the important challenge of retaining control when playing at different levels.

Andrew Tween/ Jonathan Taylor Good Gadd

The opening two-bar drum solo requires control in the ghost notes and accurate placement of syncopated accents against the time.

From letter A the challenge of this piece is to pull out the accents from the ghosted notes with the left hand whilst keeping a steady, even dynamic with the right hand.

From letter C the first theme returns with an option to ad lib, either staying on the hi hat or moving to the ride cymbal. Another way to ad lib would be to re-voice some of the accents using different drums or cymbals.

Aim to serve the music and the groove.

Graeme Taylor/ Matt McDonough So It Is

Written in the style of Chick Corea's 1980s quintets, *So It Is* gives the drummer an opportunity to display a number of solos over backings from the band, whilst additionally laying down up-tempo swing and using left hand comping to add colour and interest to the piece.

The drum chart is scored out in the style of a big band arrangement. This leaves lots of space for the drummer's interpretation. Note the style direction in the top left and add to that the figures noted above the stave, which should be played on the kit using any combination of drums/cymbals appropriate to the style and within the context of the music.

There are opportunities for 'set ups', in bar 36 for example. A set up is a technique on the drums, usually consisting of a fill to anticipate an accent played by the band.

Some fantastic examples of set ups in a big band jazz context can be heard on The Buddy Rich Big Band album *Big Swing Face*.

(*Continued overleaf*)

Bars 41-44 contain some very important triplet crotchets/quarter notes played between the hands and feet. Concentrate on clarity and orchestration in order to place these notes accurately with the ensemble.

At 255 bpm, this is a fast swing feel – time is of utmost importance when it comes to performing this successfully. Make efforts to practise up-tempo swing time away from the piece itself, in order to feel truly comfortable with playing at such a speed.

Listen to jazz/fusion drummer Dave Weckl's playing in Chick Corea's Akoustic and Elektric bands for guidance on style and touch.

Troy Miller — Jaxon's Jump

The emphasis here should be on accuracy and articulation of rhythms. Try not to miss details in dynamics and sticking as these pointers will help the feel. This form of music is loud by nature so you might want to think about damping the drums (with moon gel or tape) to make them sound more controlled and tight. Make sure everything is centred around the bass drum, as this is integral to the style. References: Jazz Steppa, Lady Leshurr and Wretch 32.

Pete Riley/ Andy Staples — Undertow

The modern progressive rock band Tool are the main inspiration for this piece along with the band's drummer Danny Carey. Like many Tool tracks this is in an odd time signature and features $\frac{7}{8}$ throughout.

The pulse is based around two crotchets/quarter notes followed by two dotted quavers/eighth notes. This rhythm is a popular way of subdividing $\frac{7}{8}$, with the kick and snare during the main groove in bar 9 essentially playing this pulse. This approach of moving the second backbeat of each bar back by a semiquaver/sixteenth note from the more obvious placement on the late quaver/eighth note has a syncopated yet smoother sound. Also at this point in the piece it's used in conjunction with a crotchet/quarter note accented right hand pattern where the accents play downbeats during one bar which move to upbeats during the next. This 'over-riding' approach again can have a smoothing effect on the potentially odd-sounding meter.

At the end of the piece is an opportunity to explore the pulse mentioned previously, as the drum solo section that ends the piece is played over a guitar riff based around this figure. Probably the best approach here would to be to keep initial ideas simple, perhaps just outlining the rhythmic figures played by the band first and then gradually building towards more demanding ideas once you're confident that you're locking in with the hits.

Pete Riley — 9 by 3

This solo piece is in $\frac{9}{8}$, and explores subdivision of the time in a couple of different ways. One recurring theme is the use of groups of three semiquavers/sixteenth notes which, with a bit of simple maths, means they fit six times in the space of one bar and create a 6 over 9 cross-rhythm, essentially like six dotted quavers/eighth notes. This can be seen during the intro where it is broken up between the double-stops and flams with the hands and bass drum.

The other is the idea of emphasising crotchets/quarter notes in the right hand during a groove which if allowed to continue over the barline then becomes the upbeat every other bar. This approach is sometimes referred to as over-riding and can have a smoothing out effect upon grooves in odd time signatures.

As a challenge and to familiarise yourself with both ideas you could practise playing the dotted quaver/eighth note rhythm on the bass drum whilst playing quavers/eighth notes in the right hand and a 2 and 4 backbeat on the snare. If done in $\frac{9}{8}$ it should a create a challenging groove that would prove helpful when tackling this piece.

Ralph Salmins — Line 'em Up

This is a piece of music in linear style. Linear is a concept in which the hands and feet play single surfaces in flowing lines creating a clean, contemporary sound.

Vinnie Colaiuta, Dave Garibaldi and Mike Clark are masters of this style. Listen to any of Vinnie's recordings with Sting to hear what he's up to. Similarly, Dave Garibaldi's funky playing on the Tower Of Power recordings such as *Drop It In The Slot* and *On The Serious Side* from their 1975 *In The Slot* album. Vinnie Colaiuta's teacher from Berklee College of Music, Gary Chaffee, has written some seminal books on the topic of linear playing and these are highly recommended as source material.

The piece starts with a hand pattern on the snare drum which then moves to the hi hat and the hands split between the two voices while adding the bass drum. It is important to be relaxed and try to get the accented notes out, while keeping unaccented notes quiet. Keep the patterns rolling and try to play as smoothly as possible while maintaining a funky feel. Don't forget to practise these patterns very slowly at first so they sink in.

Grade 8

Paul Francis — Exercise no. 1

This is a groove-based exercise in $\frac{6}{8}$ time. The time pattern should be played with purpose and a clear sense of the semiquaver/sixteenth note pulse within. In the rudimental ideas ensure that hands are balanced, feet and hands are strictly aligned, grace notes are clearly contrasted, double sticking is open and not buzzed and that dynamic contrast from bar 17 is very clear and consistent.

Paul Francis — Exercise no. 2

In the first 16 bars of this exercise various paradiddle ideas occur over a tricky foot ostinato. Practise the individual patterns first, though trust that the whole passage can flow comfortably when the challenges of independence have been met. Subsequent double sticking should be consistent in terms of time and volume and the final three paradiddle ideas, in hands *and* feet should be clearly and distinctly projected. Work on these individually at slow tempos to build confidence.

Paul Francis — Exercise no. 3

This exercise makes extensive use of the paradiddle-diddle, largely in $\frac{7}{8}$ time and thus often phasing against the hi hat with foot. The hands should be evenly balanced around the drums and all dynamics/accents should be strictly observed. The paradiddle-diddle patterns can be grouped together to make passages flow more easily; from bar 5 think pattern twice, then RLL, pattern three times, RLL, pattern once. This can be a simpler way to manage longer ideas which can at first glance seem a little austere.

Pete Riley/Andy Staples — Frantic

This track draws its inspiration from bands such as Coheed & Cambria, The Mars Volta and Panic! At The Disco, along with drummers such as Jon Theodore, Danny Carey and Gavin Harrison.

A double pedal isn't essential for playing the piece though there are occasional uses of it on the demo recording. The first is at the end of the second bridge where its use at the end of a fill down the toms gives a powerful effect, allowing intensity to increase through to the end of the pattern. Ideas such as this can be developed by playing different combinations of single strokes between the hands and feet with the hands moving between the toms and snare.

In the solo section from D, it can be very tempting to go in all guns blazing like the solo on the track. It's probably a better idea to start simply, really familiarising yourself with the placement of the figures first, perhaps beginning with a simple half-time groove to allow you to get a feel for the space you've got to work with and then gradually adding more solo orientated ideas.

Neil Robinson/John Dutton — Odd One Out

A jazz funk tune set in a $\frac{7}{8}$ time signature with a semiquaver/sixteenth note feel inspired by classic film/TV themes from the 1970s such as Starsky and Hutch and Dirty Harry. There's plenty of room to improvise during the flute and drum solo sections.

Ralph Salmins — Brazil Overture

Inspired by Earth, Wind & Fire, Steely Dan, Sergio Mendes, Steve Gadd and Chick Corea, this overture covers a wide stylistic area, featuring in particular the music of Brazil.

The piece starts with a fanfare and $\frac{5}{4}$ build-up into some changes of time incorporating phrasing over those meters. This is followed by a funk intro, leading to up-tempo funk *à la* Earth, Wind & Fire. Try to make this as tight and crisp as you can while maintaining plenty of punch. The groove should not be interrupted while observing the phrasing.

The half-time funk shuffle at bar 38 was the groove made famous by Bernard Purdie on Steely Dan's *Babylon Sisters*. Have brushes ready for the following jazz waltz, the bridge of this section metrically modulates so the previous dotted crotchet becomes the new minim, giving a natural transition to a double-time feel on sticks.

(Continued overleaf)

The following batucada passage inspired by Sergio Mendes' album *Brazileiro* and leads to a samba-funk groove made famous by Steve Gadd. The ride and bell are played with the right hand and the hi hat with the left hand, bringing the right hand back to the snare drum for the back beats. Work on this slowly until the hands gel with the samba foot pattern.

Next is the beginning of the build for the coda, starting with some phrasing and a Brazilian partito alto rhythm to be filled out and ghosted around. For the final section, build the excitement and bring out the off-beat pedal notes, quaver phrasing and solo fills.

Dave Weckl/ Steve Weingart — Crossing Paths

A contemporary jazz funk piece employing 4/4 swing and an Afro-Cuban 12/8 feel with solos. At letter C it may help to keep the fast triplet feel in your head as the subdivision (actually singing it while you keep 4/4 going in your foot is good practice, off the kit) so it becomes a definite 4 over 3. You will need a mounted cowbell for this piece.

Neil Robinson — Fusion Illusion

After a brief introduction, this piece sets off with a Jazz/Funk fusion groove made up by a four-bar phrase starting in 3/4 time with the fourth bar in 2/4 creating an interesting groove. The grace notes really add to the feel and are to be played lightly leaning more towards being an embellishment. The open hi hats should be kept tight and crisp.

It then moves to a 6/4 section adding in an Afro-beat element to the funky fusion feel.

After an improvised solo section it then returns to the 3/4 time signature but, this time, with a 4 against 3 feel. The challenging underlying theme now, until the end of the piece, is where the dominant groove switches between the 3 and 4 feel. Try to stretch out the buzz on beat 3 of bar 25 with the grace note drag on the end still being minutely separated using the up stroke.

Think of the sticking for the big ending fill at bar 43 as being paradiddle-based with an extra note added i.e. RLLRRLRLL etc. which turns it into a nine stroke triplet feel. Use bounce for the speed.

Jon Whitfield — Turkish Delight

The piece uses the Dave Brubeck Quartet's *Blue Rondo a la Turk* as a way to explore a 2223 grouping in 9/8 time. Parts of Brubeck's composition are referenced throughout and familiarity with this tune is useful when preparing a performance of *Turkish Delight*.

After an initial funk section we move to snare and toms at bar 25 using open five stroke rolls for the semiquavers/ sixteenth notes. A songo in 3/4 is introduced at bar 33.

Bars 41–48 have a slow 3/4 funk groove played six times over the eight bars of nine. This idea is extended to 4/4 at bar 49 which begins a phasing effect across the solid 9/8 pulse in the hi hat. Try to keep feeling the compound time in this tricky section.

At bar 57 we return to the main theme keeping the left hand on the snare and playing the melody with the right.

This page has been left blank to facilitate page turns.

Grades 7 and 8 Rudiments

You will need to learn the rudiments up to Grade 6 and the following to be able to play the Exercises for Grades 7 and 8.

Pata fla fla

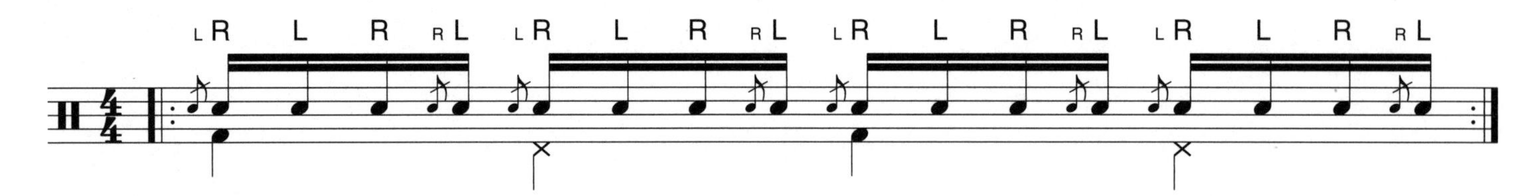

Swiss army triplet

Inward paradiddle

If you are left handed you may reverse the sticking.

Candidates must prepare all three exercises, but only two will be played during the exam. One is chosen by the candidate, the other by the examiner. (If you are left handed you may reverse the sticking.)

Track 1 – Demo 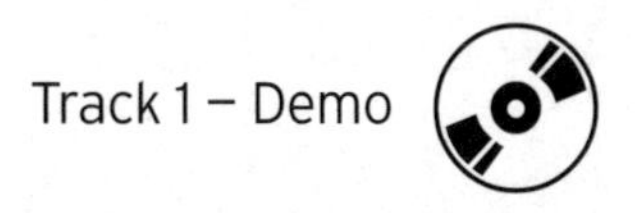

Grade 7 Exercises

Exercise no. 1

Paul Francis

Remember to look at the Performance Notes on pages 5-8

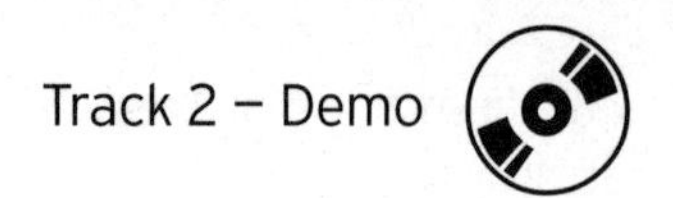

Exercise no. 2

Paul Francis

Remember to look at the Performance Notes on pages 5–8

Exercise no. 3

Paul Francis

Remember to look at the Performance Notes on pages 5-8

Track 4 – Demo
Track 5 – With click
Track 6 – Without click

Good Gadd

Andrew Tween/Jonathan Taylor

This piece can be performed in the exam with *either* the CD backing track, *or* with a live accompanist using the supplied piano part.

Remember to look at the Performance Notes on pages 5–8

Track 7 – Demo
Track 8 – With click
Track 9 – Without click

So It Is

Graeme Taylor/Matt McDonough

You may photocopy this page to avoid a page turn.

* = performer's choice of drum(s) to be played using the rhythm shown.

SOLO FILLS around optional figures

77

mf *(Build intensity each repeat)*

81

x3

Cont. FILLS

85

ff

89

D.S. al Coda

Coda

93

mf

SOLO FILLS around optional figures

97

101

f

105

108

ff

Remember to look at the Performance Notes on pages 5-8

Track 10 – Demo
Track 11 – With click
Track 12 – Without click

Jaxon's Jump

Troy Miller

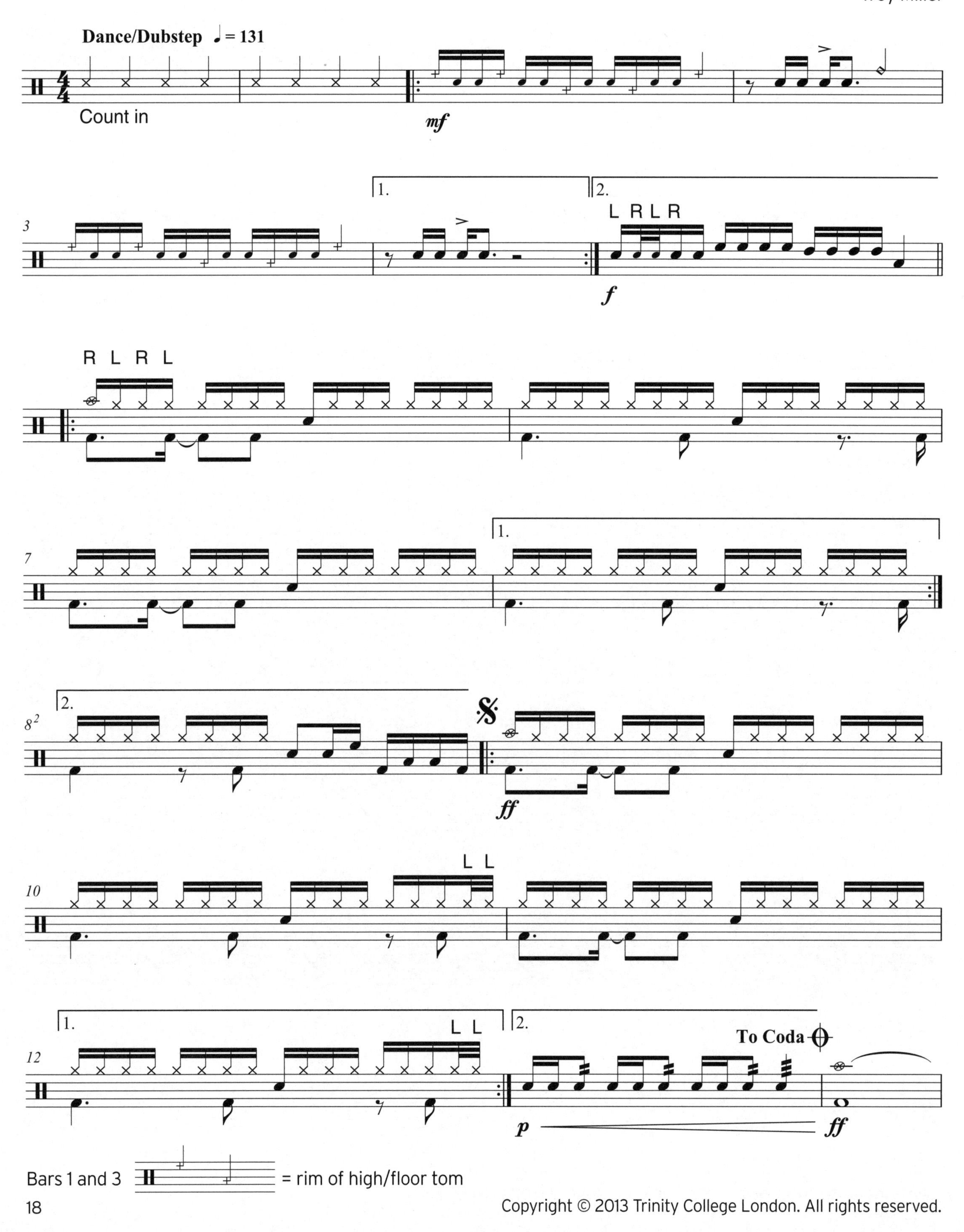

Remember to look at the Performance Notes on pages 5-8

Track 13 – Demo
Track 14 – With click
Track 15 – Without click

Undertow

Pete Riley/Andy Staples

Remember to look at the Performance Notes on pages 5-8

* = performer's choice of drum(s) to be played using the rhythm shown.

Track 16 – Demo 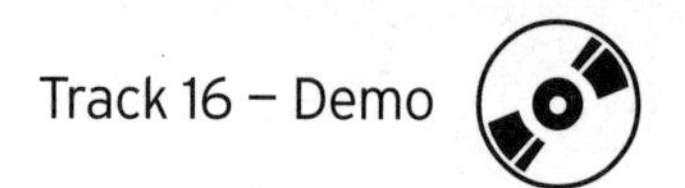

9 by 3

Pete Riley

Remember to look at the Performance Notes on pages 5-8

Track 17 – Demo 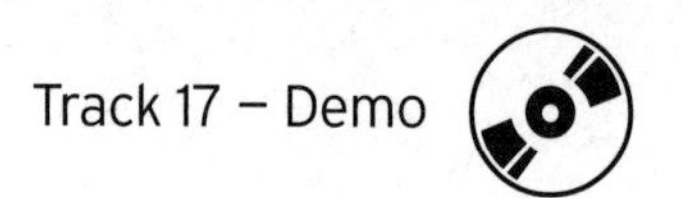

Line 'em Up

Ralph Salmins

Drum Kit 4

Piano accompaniment

for Trinity College London exams
2014–2019

Grades 7 & 8

Published by
Trinity College London
Registered Office:
89 Albert Embankment
London SE1 7TP UK
T +44 (0)20 7820 6100
F +44 (0)20 7820 6161
E music@trinitycollege.co.uk
www.trinitycollege.co.uk

Registered in the UK
Company no. 02683033
Charity no. 1014792

Second impression, April 2014

Music processed by Moira Roach.
Piano part supplied by www.grooveworld.co.uk
Printed in England by Halstan, Amersham, Bucks.

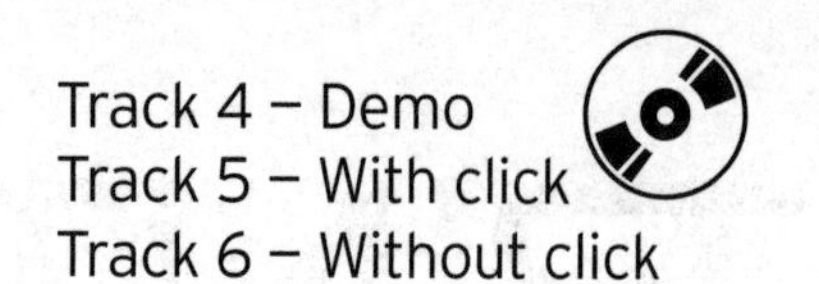

Good Gadd

Andrew Tween/Jonathan Taylor

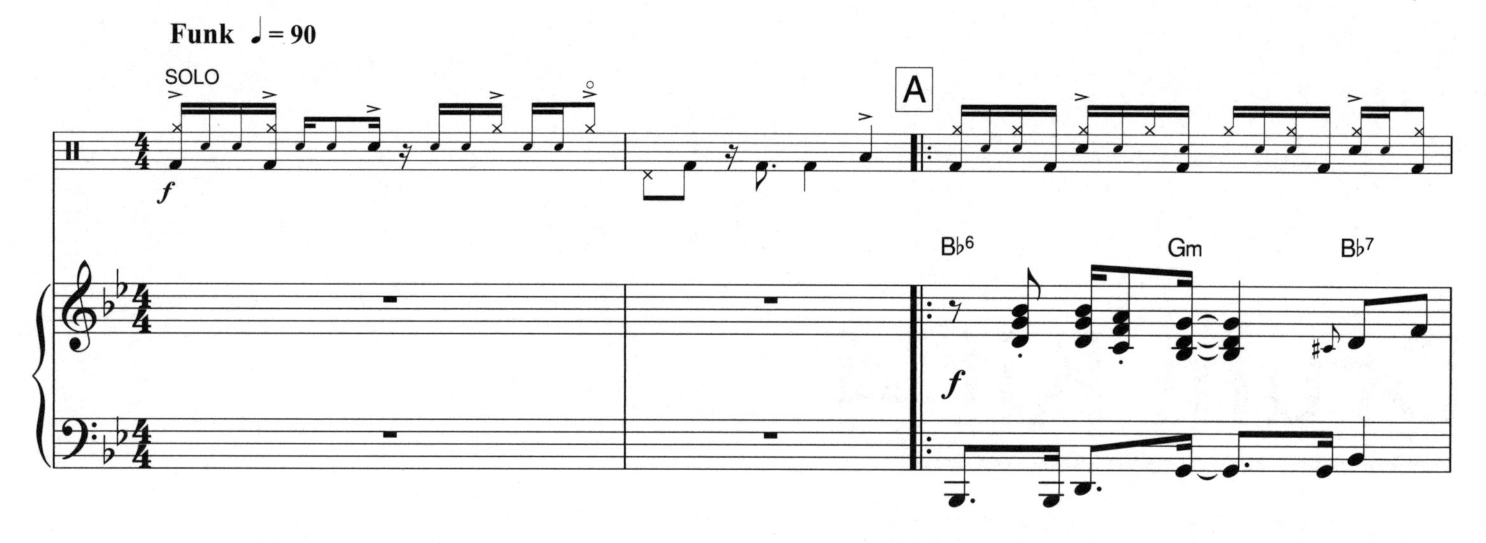

1.
9
Eb/G Gb7 Eb/F E7(#11) Eb7
Eb7 E7 F7
2.
9 2
Eb/G Gb7 Eb/F E7(#11) Eb7
mf
B
Bb Eb/G Ab7 A7(#11)
12
Bb Eb/G F#7 F7
Bb Eb7 D7(#9) G7(#11) C7
Eb/F
15
Bb Eb/G Ab7 A7(#11)
Bb Eb/G F#7 F7

17
B♭
E♭7
D7(♯9)
G7(♯11)
C7
F7(SUS4)
19
C
ad lib.
B♭6
Gm
B♭7
f
E♭maj7
Dm7
C7
F13
21
Dm11
A♭7
Gm7
Am11
D7
Gm
B♭7
24
E♭maj7
G♭/A♭
E♭/G
G♭7
E♭/F
E7(♯11)
E♭7
A♭7
A7
B♭7

Remember to look at the Performance Notes on pages 5–8

Candidates must prepare all three exercises, but only two will be played during the exam. One is chosen by the candidate, the other by the examiner. (If you are left handed you may reverse the sticking.)

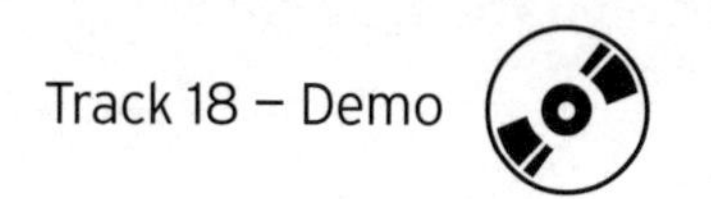

Grade 8 Exercises

Exercise no. 1

Paul Francis

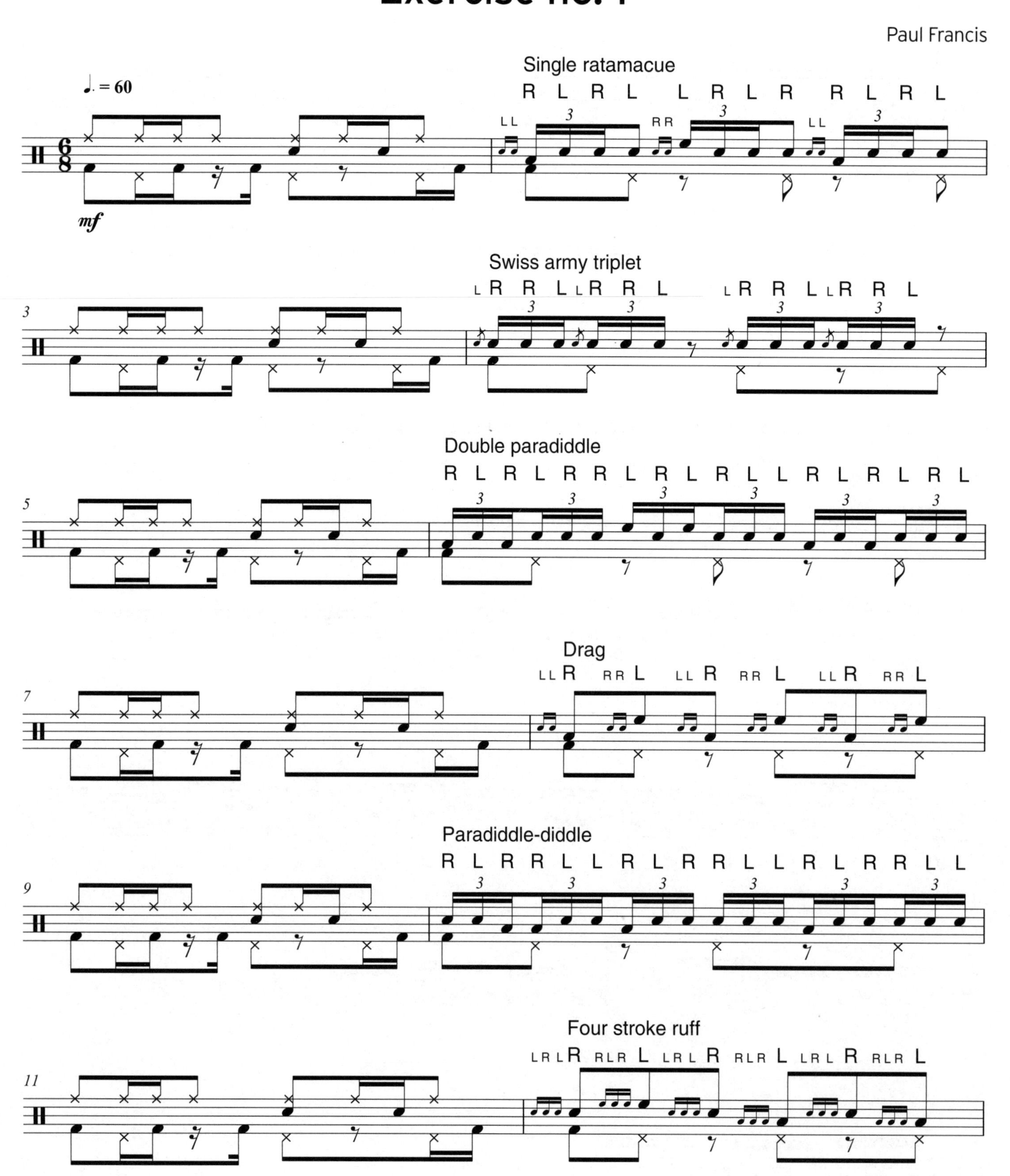

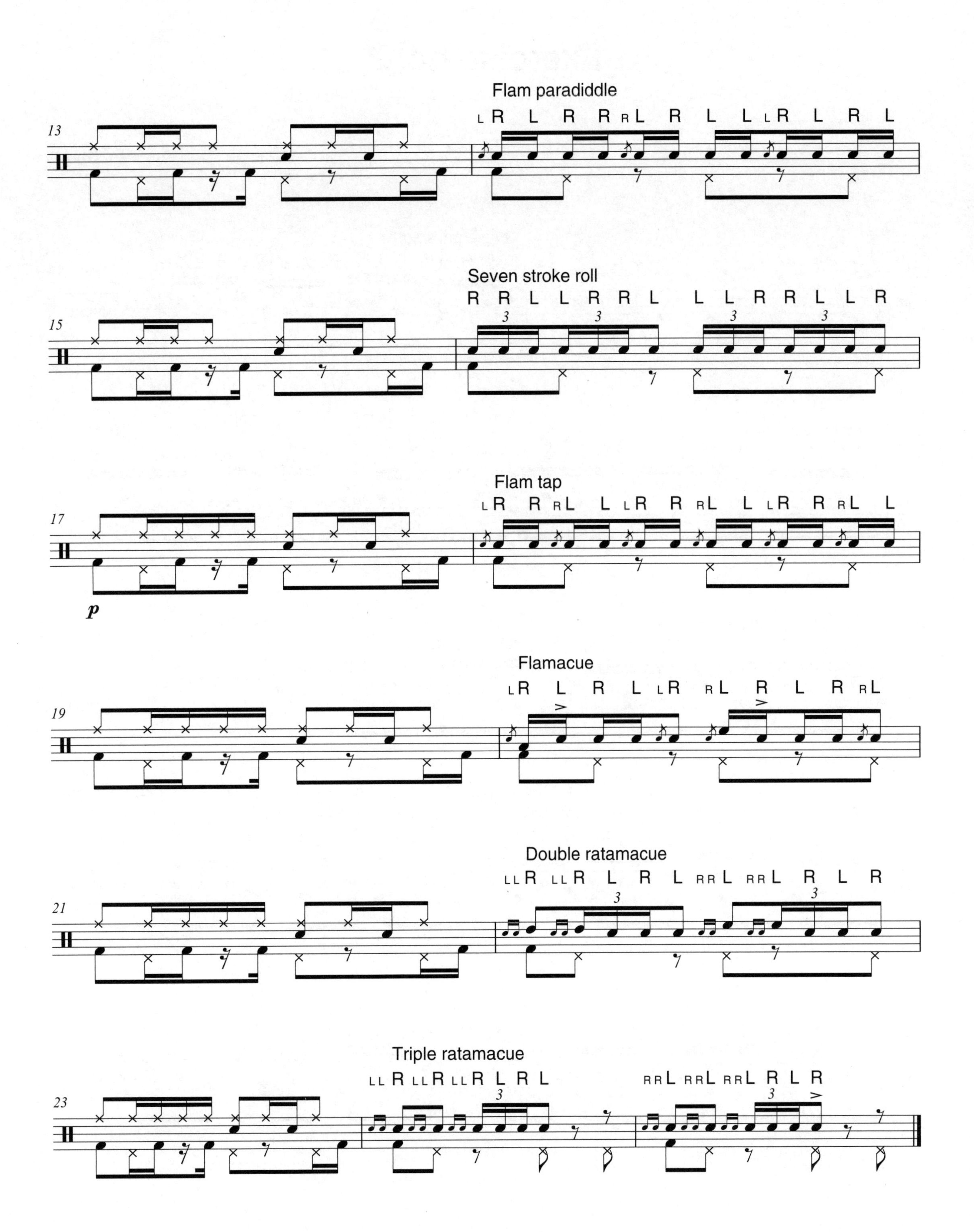
13
Flam paradiddle
LR L R R RL R L L LR L R L
15
Seven stroke roll
R R L L R R L L L R R L L R
17
Flam tap
LR R RL L LR R RL L LR R RL L
19
Flamacue
LR L R L LR RL R L R RL
21
Double ratamacue
LLR LLR L R L RRL RRL R L R
23
Triple ratamacue
LL R LLR LLR L R L RRL RRL RRL R L R

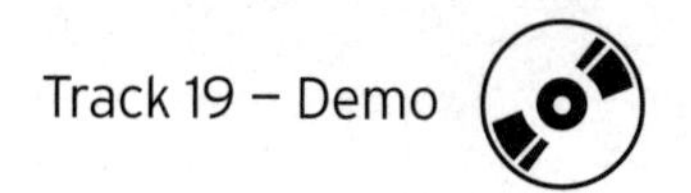

Exercise no. 2

Paul Francis

Remember to look at the Performance Notes on pages 5-8

Exercise no. 3

Paul Francis

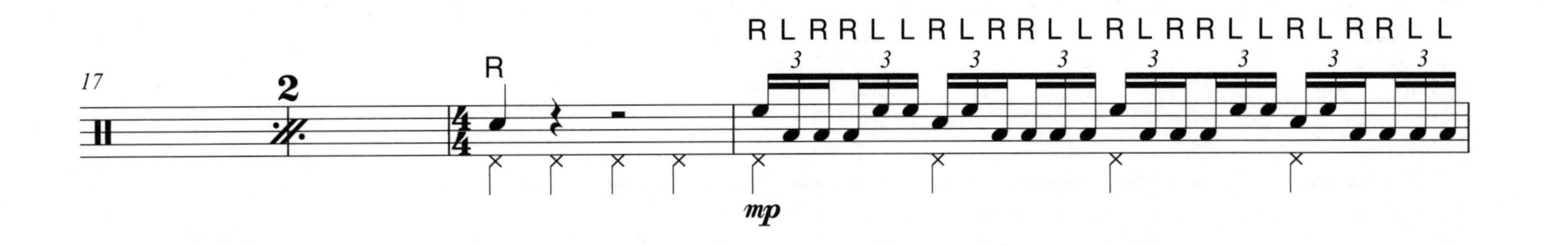

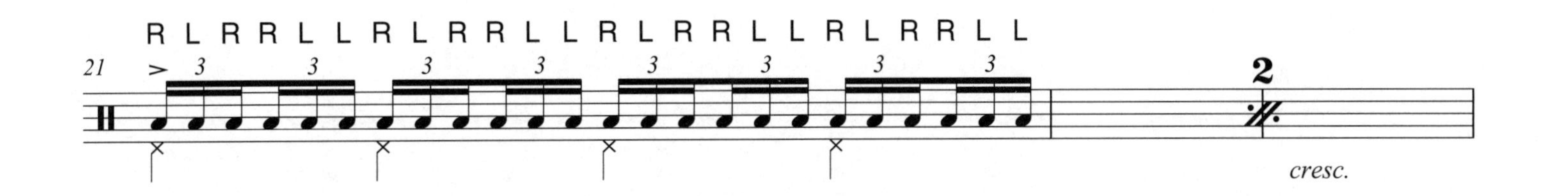

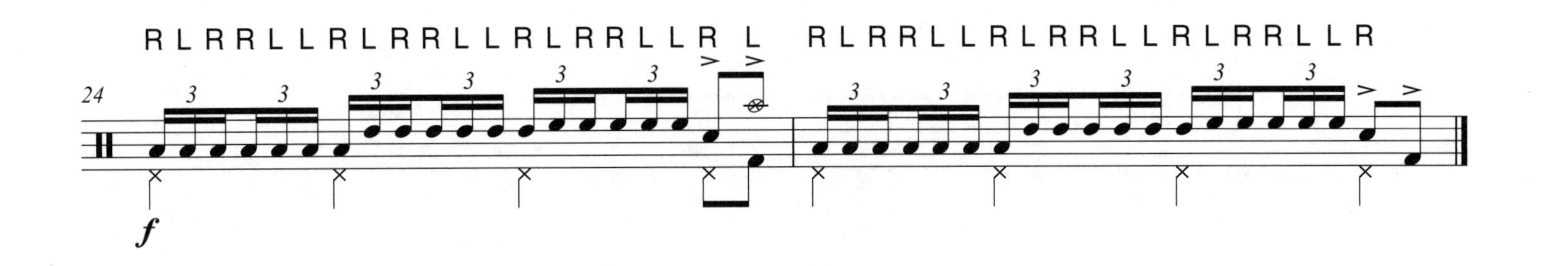

Remember to look at the Performance Notes on pages 5-8

Track 21 – Demo
Track 22 – With click
Track 23 – Without click

Frantic

Pete Riley/Andy Staples

Remember to look at the Performance Notes on pages 5-8

* = performer's choice of drum(s) to be played using the rhythm shown.

You may photocopy this page to avoid a page turn.

This page has been left blank to facilitate page turns.

Track 24 – Demo
Track 25 – With click
Track 26 – Without click

Odd One Out

Neil Robinson/John Dutton

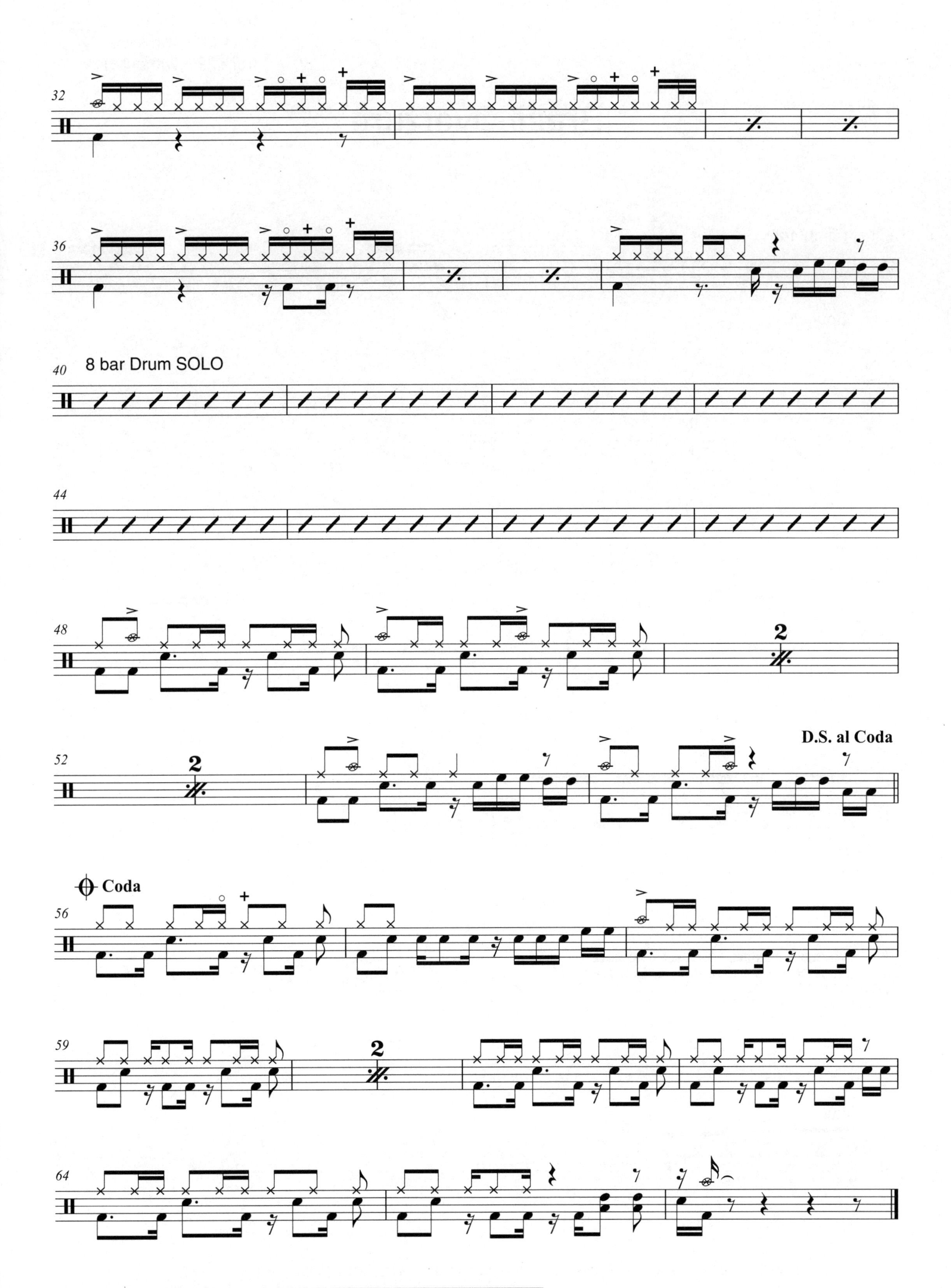

Remember to look at the Performance Notes on pages 5-8

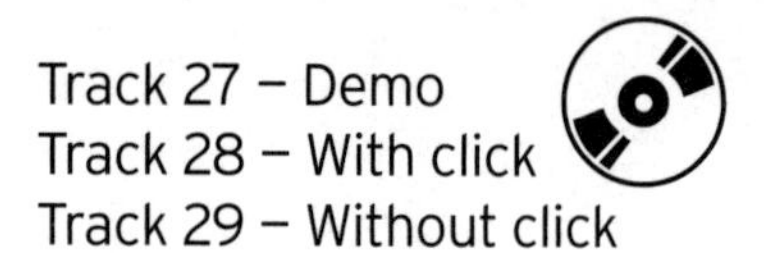

Brazil Overture

Ralph Salmins

* = performer's choice of drum(s) to be played using the rhythm shown.

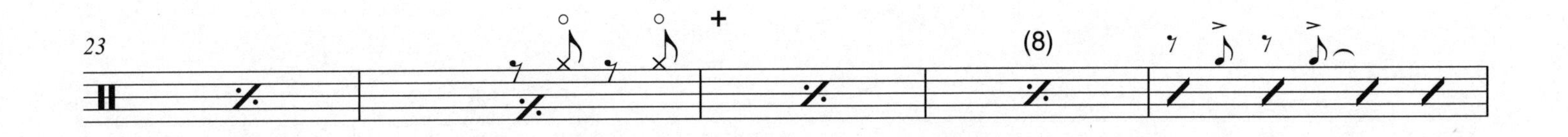

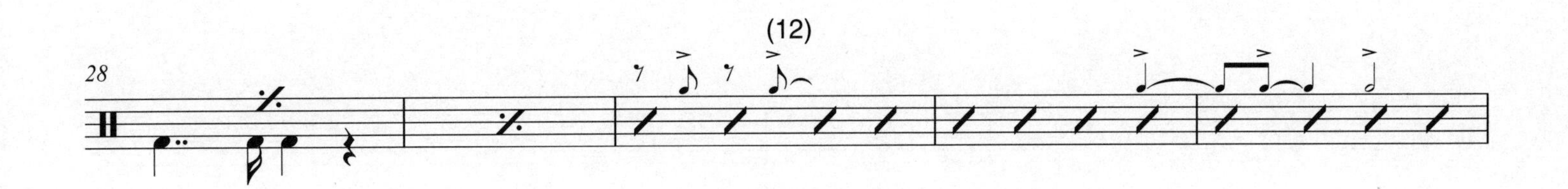

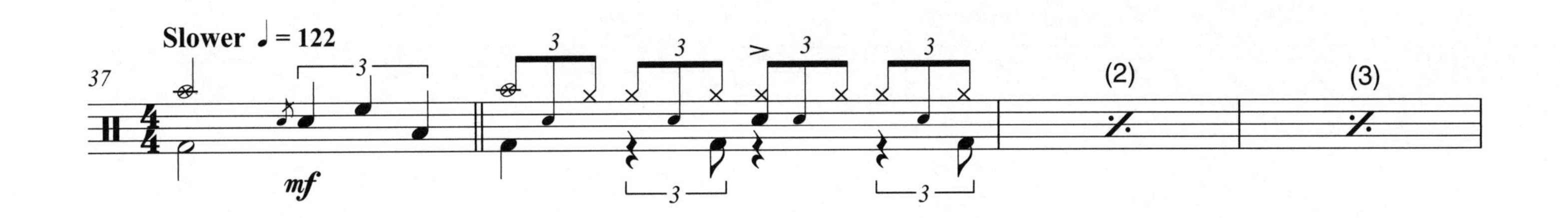

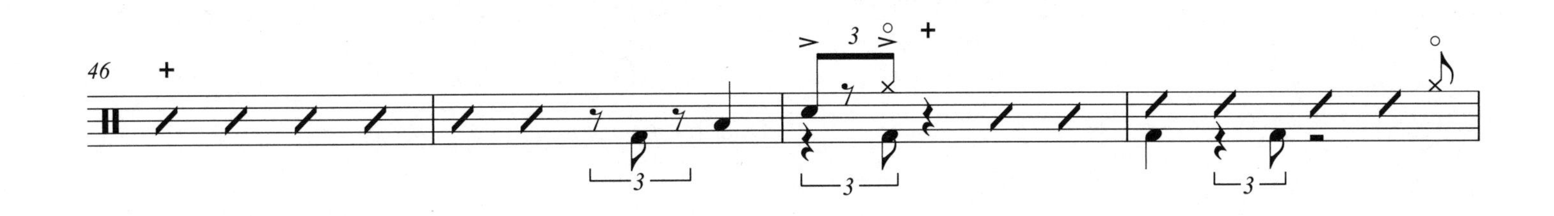

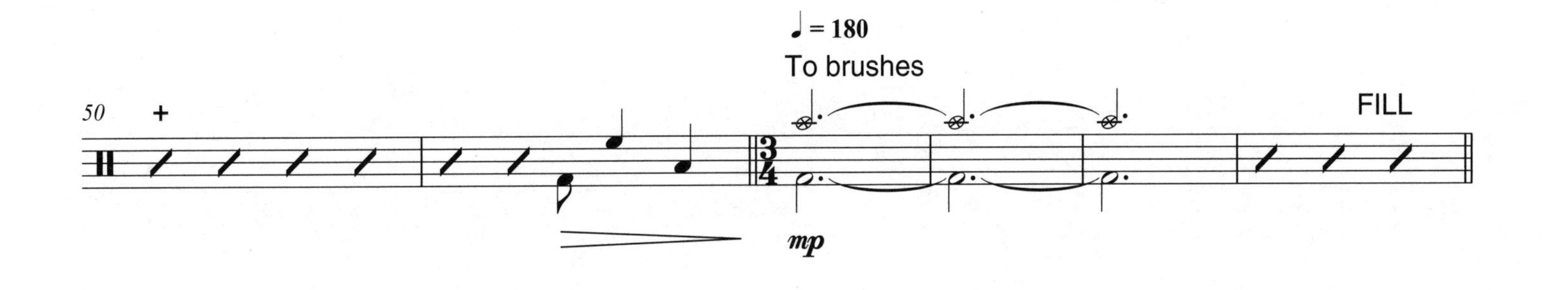

Remember to look at the Performance Notes on pages 5-8

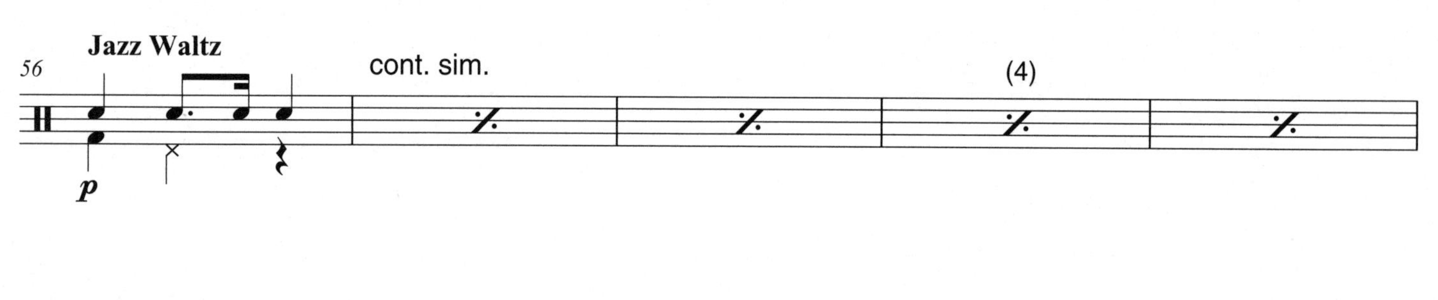

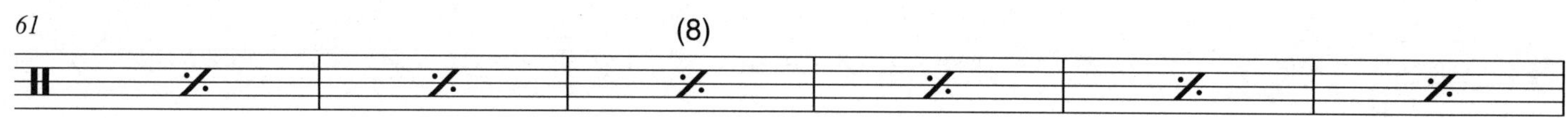

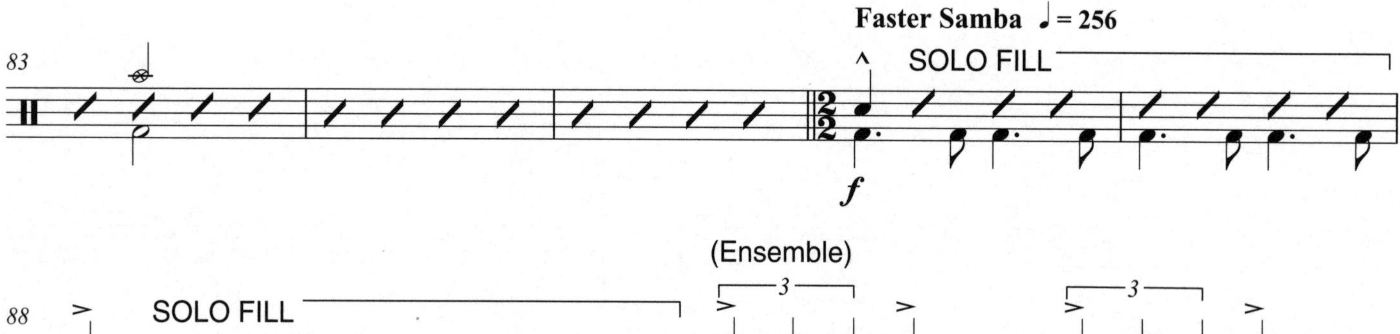

You may photocopy this page to avoid a page turn.

You may photocopy this page to avoid a page turn.

Track 30 – Demo
Track 31 – With click

Crossing Paths

Dave Weckl/Steve Weingart

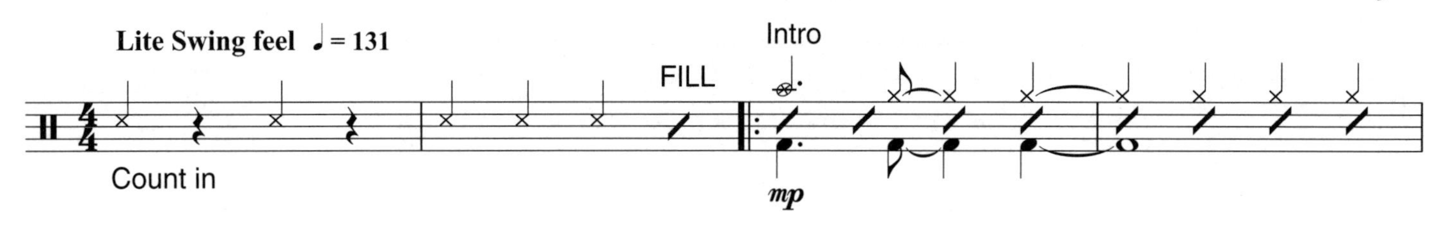

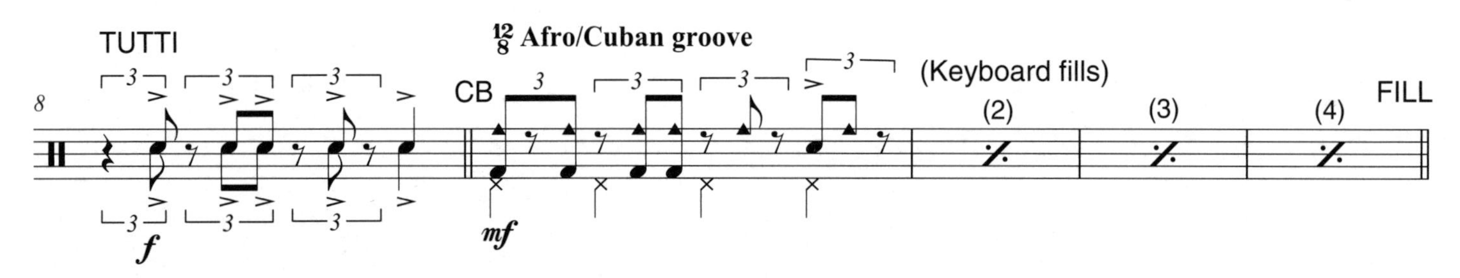

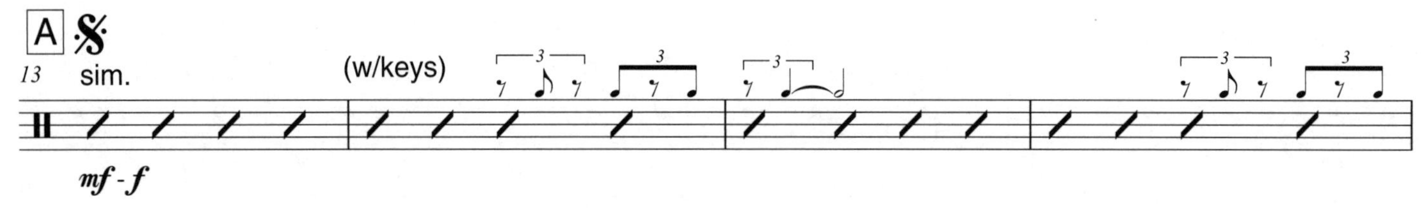

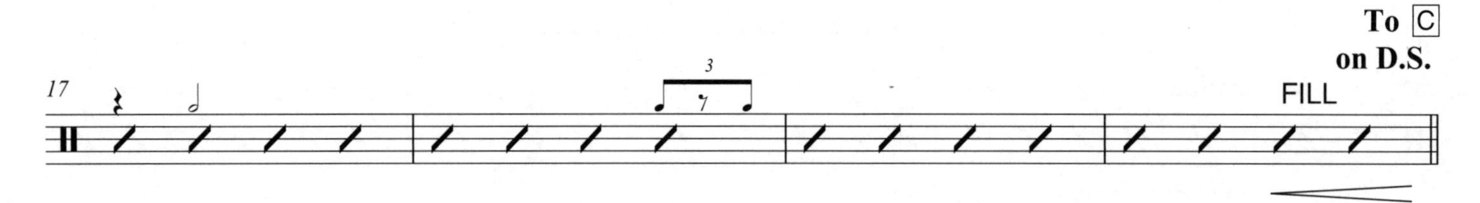

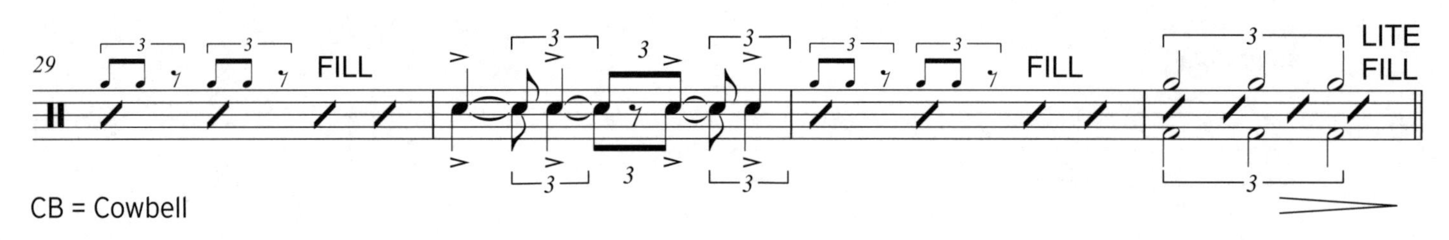

CB = Cowbell

Remember to look at the Performance Notes on pages 5-8

Track 32 – Demo

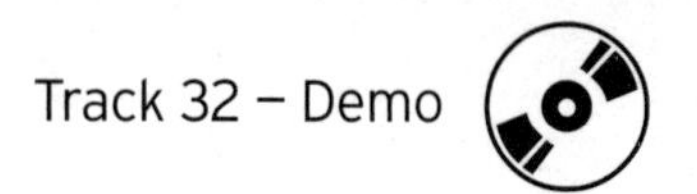

Fusion Illusion

Neil Robinson

* N.B. fourth time bar is in $\frac{4}{4}$

Remember to look at the Performance Notes on pages 5-8

Turkish Delight

Jon Whitfield

Remember to look at the Performance Notes on pages 5-8

Quasi songo
Splash with foot
R L R L L R L L
L L L L L L
x3*
* Second time play
Third time play

CD track listing

Grade 7

1.	Exercise no. 1	Francis	0'41"
2.	Exercise no. 2	Francis	0'37"
3.	Exercise no. 3	Francis	0'45"
4.	Good Gadd	Tween/Taylor	1'36"
5.	Good Gadd (backing track with click)	Tween/Taylor	1'39"
6.	Good Gadd (backing track without click)	Tween/Taylor	1'39"
7.	So It Is	Taylor/McDonough	2'34"
8.	So It Is (backing track with click)	Taylor/McDonough	2'36"
9.	So It Is (backing track without click)	Taylor/McDonough	2'36"
10.	Jaxon's Jump	Miller	2'03"
11.	Jaxon's Jump (backing track with click)	Miller	2'06"
12.	Jaxon's Jump (backing track without click)	Miller	2'06"
13.	Undertow	Riley/Staples	2'36"
14.	Undertow (backing track with click)	Riley/Staples	2'41"
15.	Undertow (backing track without click)	Riley/Staples	2'41"
16.	9 by 3	Riley	1'35"
17.	Line 'em Up	Salmins	1'36"

Grade 8

18.	Exercise no. 1	Francis	0'54"
19.	Exercise no. 2	Francis	1'05"
20.	Exercise no. 3	Francis	1'17"
21.	Frantic	Riley/Staples	2'28"
22.	Frantic (backing track with click)	Riley/Staples	2'31"
23.	Frantic (backing track without click)	Riley/Staples	2'31"
24.	Odd One Out	Robinson/Dutton	2'56"
25.	Odd One Out (backing track with click)	Robinson/Dutton	3'00"
26.	Odd One Out (backing track without click)	Robinson/Dutton	3'00"
27.	Brazil Overture	Salmins	2'55"
28.	Brazil Overture (backing track with click)	Salmins	2'55"
29.	Brazil Overture (backing track without click)	Salmins	2'55"
30.	Crossing Paths	Weckl/Weingart	3'09"
31.	Crossing Paths (backing track with click)	Weckl/Weingart	3'12"
32.	Fusion Illusion	Robinson	1'57"
33.	Turkish Delight	Whitfield	1'45"